Submarine Adventure

Roderick Hunt   Alex Brychta

Characters

Narrator

Wilf

Chip

Biff

Professor Tangle

Wilma

Scene 1

Narrator   Scene 1   'Biff's room'
Wilf was excited.

Wilf   Look what I had for my birthday.

Narrator   Wilf opened a box.

Chip   What is it?

Biff   *(gasps)*   Is it a submarine?

Narrator	Biff and Chip looked at it.
Chip	It looks odd.
Wilf	It's a kind of submarine. It explores the sea bed.
Wilma	That's right. It goes to the bottom of the sea.

Biff   It has windows.

Wilma   And it has headlights.
               The headlights light up.
               Put them on, Wilf.

Narrator   Wilf put the headlights on.

Chip   It's brilliant.

Narrator   Suddenly the magic key began to glow.

Chip	Look. The key is glowing.
Biff	We're off on a magic adventure.
Wilf	I wonder where the key will take us.

(sound of magic working)

Wilma	We're getting smaller.
Biff	The magic is taking us through the door of the little house.

Scene 2

Narrator   Scene 2   'The submarine'
The magic took them to the sea.

Biff   What's that strange-looking boat?
It looks like a submarine.

Wilma   It looks like Wilf's toy submarine.

Narrator   The children were excited.

Chip	This is exciting. I wish we could look inside it.
Narrator	A door in the submarine began to open.
Wilf	Look! Someone is coming out of the submarine.
Biff	Who can it be?

Scene 3

Narrator   Scene 3   'Professor Tangle'
A man looked out of the submarine.

Tangle   Hello! Hello! I'm Professor Tangle.
Who are you?

Wilf   How do you do.

Tangle   Who? My new crew?
You look a bit young.

Narrator	Professor Tangle couldn't hear. He got things muddled up.
Chip	We are not your crew.
Tangle	You know what to do? You'd better get on board, then. What are your names?
Biff	I am Biff. This is Chip.

Tangle	No, it's not really a ship.
	It's a diving machine.
Wilf	I'm Wilf and this is Wilma.
Wilma	*(shouts)* We are not your new crew.
Tangle	You flew?
	I didn't see an aeroplane.
	Well, get on board.

Scene 4

Narrator   Scene 4   'Inside the submarine'

Wilma   *(whispers)*   There is not much room.

Narrator   Professor Tangle shut the door.

Tangle   It's time to start the engines.

Biff   I hope the submarine doesn't leak.

Tangle   Of course you can speak.
It's time to dive.

Narrator   The submarine began to dive.

(There is a loud bubbling sound.)

Tangle   Push that button, Biff.
Press that handle, Wilf.
Pull that lever, Chip.

Narrator The submarine began to go down.
It went deeper and deeper.

Chip *(shouts)* Where are we heading?
Will we dive deep?

Tangle No, you can't go to sleep.
We are going to dive deep.

Wilma This thing scares me.

Scene 5

Narrator   Scene 5   'The sea bed'
The submarine went down to the sea bed.
Everyone looked out of the window.

Wilma   I can see a shark.

Tangle   Yes, it is getting dark.

Chip   How deep are we going?

(There is a bubbling sound.)

Narrator	The submarine went even deeper. Professor Tangle was excited.
Tangle	*(excitedly)* We are near the sea bed.
Biff	It's getting very dark. Put the lights on, Professor.
Tangle	No, no. I'll put the lights on. Bother. I can't get them to work.

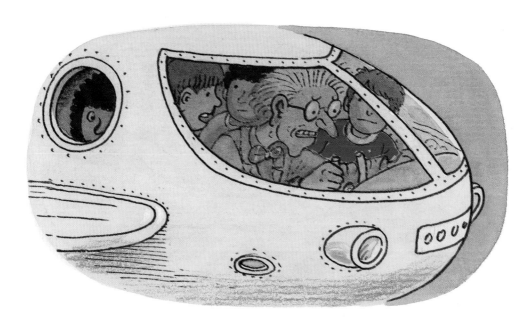

Biff   Oh no! I can see huge rocks.

Wilf   *(gasps)*   We are heading straight for them.

Tangle   I've got a spare fuse somewhere.

Wilma   *(shouts loudly)*   WE ARE HEADING FOR SOME ROCKS!

Tangle   No, I don't need clean socks.

Chip   Look out! We're going to crash.

Scene 6

Narrator   Scene 6   'The diamond cave'
The submarine didn't crash.
It just missed the rocks.

Wilma   *(puffs)*   Phew! That was close.

Wilf   *(looking)*   What's that ahead?

Chip   It's a cave.

Tangle	*(holding up a fuse)* I've found it at last.
Wilf	*(shouts)* WE ARE HEADING FOR A CAVE. SLOW DOWN, PROFESSOR.
Tangle	My goodness! We must slow down. Pull that lever, Wilf.
Narrator	The submarine slowed down. It went into the cave.

Chip	This cave is amazing.
Biff	It is so big. I wish it wasn't so dark.
Tangle	I'll see if this new fuse works.
Narrator	Professor Tangle put on the headlights.
Tangle	Hooray! Fixed them at last.

Narrator	The headlights lit up the cave. The walls gleamed.
Tangle	*(excitedly)* There are diamonds all over the walls of the cave.
Everyone	*(together)* Diamonds!
Tangle	*(crazily)* I'm rich! I'm rich!
Biff	But you can't get the diamonds.

Tangle   What was that? Speak up.

Everyone   YOU CAN'T GET THE DIAMONDS.

Tangle   Bother! I hadn't thought of that!

Narrator   Suddenly there was a loud noise.
The cave began to shake.

Wilma   What's happening?

Wilf   The walls of the cave are shaking.

Narrator   The roof of the cave began to fall.

Chip   Help! Rocks are falling all round us.

Tangle   We must get out!

(sound of thumps and crashes)

Tangle   Full speed! Full speed!
Let's get out of here!

Wilma   We aren't going to make it!

Wilf	Hooray! We made it!
Biff	Phew! That was close.
Chip	We're sorry about the diamonds. Nobody can get them now.
Wilma	The magic key is glowing.
Tangle	I don't think it's snowing.
Everyone	*(together)* Goodbye. It's time to go.

Narrator   The magic took them home.
It took them back to Biff's room.

Biff   That was an exciting adventure.
Professor Tangle was funny.

Wilf   *(pretends to be deaf)*   What? Eh?
I have no money.

(Everyone laughs.)